Seals

naturally scottish

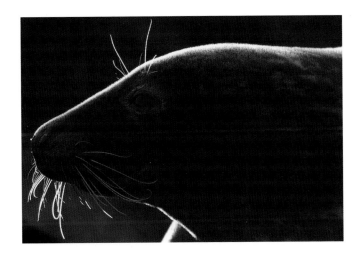

'When angels fell, some fell on the land, some on the sea.
The former are the faeries and the latter were often said to be the seals.'

Anonymous Orcadian

SCOTTISH NATURAL HERITAGE

© Scottish Natural Heritage 2007
ISBN 978 1 85397 528 8 paperback
A CIPO record is held at the British Library
BP1.5K0807

Acknowledgements: John Baxter for his advice and expertise, colleagues past and present at SMRU and Caroline Wickham-Jones.

Author: Callan Duck

Series Editor: Lynne Farrell (SNH)

Design and Production: SNH Design and Publications

Photographs:

Doug Allan/naturepl.com 4, 29 (top and bottom right); **Brandon Cole/naturepl.com** 16; **Louise Cunningham** 11 (top right and common seal coat 2, 3, 4); **Callan Duck** 24, 26 (right); **Callan Duck and Beth Mackey** opposite introduction; **Lorne Gill** opposite contents, 7 (bottom), 11 (grey seal coat images) 12, 13, 14, 26 (left), 30, 36, 37, 38, 43; **Rob Harris** 31; **Alan James/naturepl.com** 20; **Patricia and Angus Macdonald/SNH** 34; **Beth Mackey** frontispiece, 11 (common seal coat 1), 15, 25 (bottom); **Keith Much/Crown copyright, FRS Marine Laboratory** 21; **Andrew Parkinson/naturepl.com** 2, 32; **Charlie Phillips** 7; **Mike Salisbury/naturepl.com** 29 (bottom left); **Kevin Schafer/NHPA/Photoshot** 29 (top left); **Anup Shah/naturepl.com** 3; **SMRU** 25 (top); **Trustees of the National Museums of Scotland** 45; **Richard Welsby** 41; **David Whitaker** contents.

Illustrations:

Vicky Ogilvy 8, 9, 10, 12, 13, 18, 19, 22, 23; **Ruth Sharples** 27.

Scottish Natural Heritage
Design and Publications
Battleby
Redgorton
Perth PH1 3EW
Tel: 01738 444177
Fax: 01738 827411
E-mail: pubs@snh.gov.uk
Website: http://www.snh.org.uk

Cover photograph:
Female grey seal
Frontispiece:
Profile of grey seal highlighting whiskers
Back cover photograph:
Common seal

Seals

naturally scottish

by

Callan Duck

(Sea Mammal Research Unit)

Foreword

Scotland's wild and remote coastline, with its safe inlets and secluded beaches, provides the perfect breeding ground for both common and grey seals. These bewitching sea creatures form part of the magical tapestry of my adopted homeland in the Orkney Islands.

That most eerie of sounds, the "song" of the grey seal has been the source of a lasting mythology about selkies, the Orcadian term for seals, and an inspiration to many, including myself, and my late and great friend, writer and poet, George Mackay Brown.

My piece "A Selkie Tale" is a humorous version of the Orkney folk-tale of an islander kidnapping a Selkie wife - a creature who is a seal in the sea and a woman on the land. Things go entertainingly awry - the Selkie wife escapes to rejoin her folk in the sea, and Mansie, the islander, faces a most uncongenial alliance with his cousin and housekeeper, Miss Trowie-Tattibogle.

Away from the mythology, the modern world presents many threats to the seals around our shores – from disease, natural predators and climate change to the careless disposal of chemical and other pollutants, discarded nets and willful shooting. It is so important that we understand how seals fit into the wider picture and how we impact on them, and by drawing on his wealth of experience Callan Duck's excellent book helps us to do that.

It is reassuring to know that organisations like Scottish Natural Heritage and the Sea Mammal Research Unit are monitoring and managing the habitats of seals to ensure that future generations will be able to derive as much interest and pleasure from the seals that grace our coasts and seas as we do now.

Peter Maxwell Davies.

Sir Peter Maxwell Davies
Composer

Adult common seal showing the ear behind the eye (above). Group of grey seals hauled out (opposite)

Contents

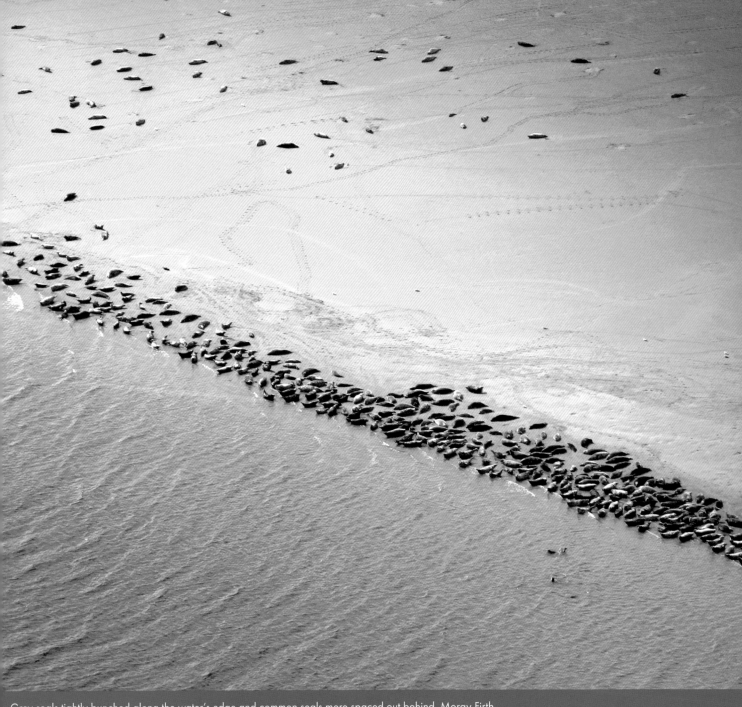

Grey seals tightly bunched along the water's edge and common seals more spaced out behind, Moray Firth

Introduction

Seals are loved by many people but not by everyone. They can evoke stong emotions and are often the centre of contoversy. They have also featured in Scottish mythology. This book is about the seals that you can see around Scotland.

What are seals?

Seals belong to a group of carniverous mammals called pinnipeds, meaning flap-footed animals. Their limbs (called flippers) and streamlined body shape have evolved for life in water.

Seals are easily divided into three distinct groups: the true seals (Phocidae), the eared seals or fur seals and sea lions (Otariidae) and the walrus (Odobaenidae). Unlike the two other groups of truly aquatic marine mammals, the whales, dolphins and porpoises and the dugongs and manatees, seals must return to land or onto ice to give birth to their pups. They also return on to land or ice at other periods during their annual cycle to moult their fur or to rest. While all seals are highly adapted to life in the water, they are not equally adapted to life on land. In fact the most obvious differences between the three groups of seal relate to the way they move in the water and on land.

Seals are not distributed evenly around the world. Most seals live in either temperate or polar regions and only three species live in tropical waters. There are 18 species of phocid or true seal, 14 species of otariid or eared seal and one species of odobaenid or walrus. Some of these species are made up of a number of subspecies; the common seal (also known as harbour seal) is one of these, with five subspecies recognised.

The fossil record shows that seals originated about 26 million years ago. There is some argument whether the three groups of seal present today evolved from one common terrestrial, ancestral carnivore or from two. The traditional view is that seals evolved from two sources. Two groups, the eared seals and walrus, evolved from a bear-like ancestor while the third, the true seals, evolved from a weasel or otter-like ancestor. The alternative, currently more favoured, option is that all seals derived from the same ancestor. Whatever their origin, walrus are the odd group, sharing certain features with the true seals and others with the eared seals.

True seals (Phocidae)

True seals, or phocids, are perhaps the most highly adapted to life in the water. On average, they can dive to deeper depths and remain under water for longer than eared seals and they are less well adapted to moving on land. They swim using alternate side-to-side strokes of their hind flippers. Their fore flippers are held tight against their bodies when swimming fast, and are occasionally used for steering when making fast turns. When swimming slowly, they may either use their hind flippers or may paddle with their fore flippers. On land, they always lie flat on their bellies, sides or backs. True seals do not move very efficiently on land – they hump along the ground, extending their head and shoulders forward and then drawing their pelvis forward, with a motion rather like that of an earthworm or caterpillar. They frequently use their fore flippers to help and you can see their tracks on a sandy beach; see photo on previous page. Although this seems rather clumsy, true seals can move extremely rapidly when necessary, appearing to bounce across the ground.

True seals do not have an ear flap, they just have a small ear hole just behind their eye. Both the fore and hind flippers are completely covered with hair and their claws extend beyond the edges. True seals cannot sit up to rest or flex their hind flippers forwards, and use only their hand-like fore flippers for scratching themselves. They have a thick layer of fat or blubber which insulates them from the cold and a coarse coat of fairly short hair which provides virtually no insulation.

Only two species of true seal breed in Scotland; common seals and grey seals, although a few more northern species occasionally visit.

Grey seal bouncing along a beach

Fur seals and sea lions (Otariidae)

This group of eared seals use their large wing or paddle-like fore flippers for swimming or flying through the water, and their hind flippers as rudders. When swimming fast, fur seals and sea lions will porpoise out of the water to take a breath of air. On land, their hind flippers can flex forwards and they walk holding their body clear of the ground. They have three points of contact with the ground: each fore flipper and their tied-at-the-ankle hind flippers. They are considerably more agile on land than true seals and can move very quickly. They have a small but conspicuous rolled ear flap. Most of the flipper is bare and the claws are close to the middle of their flippers. The claws on the fore flippers are very small and rudimentary but those on their hind flippers are long and are used for scratching. They have a thinner blubber layer than true seals and the fur seals have a thick undercoat of fur which traps an insulating layer of air when they dive. Sea lions have just a thin, single coat of hair.

Fur seals and sea lions do not occur in the wild in Scotland.

Fur seal sitting up, showing its large fore flippers and using its hind flipper for scratching

Walrus (Odobaenidae)

Walrus are very distinctive Arctic seals whose upper canines develop into highly enlarged tusks. In evolutionary terms, they seem to be intermediary between the true and eared seals, showing some of the characteristics of each group. They are not fast swimmers and swim using alternate strokes of their hind flippers. They also use their fore flippers to swim and as hydroplanes for steering.

On land, the heavy walrus are ponderous but can flex their hind flippers forwards and walk in the same manner as the eared seals, although they cannot lift their body off the ground because of their massive size. They do not have an ear flap or any hair, and all their insulation is provided by a thick layer of blubber. They use their tusks for hauling themselves onto ice floes to rest. They also use them when sifting through the sea bed sediment as they search for their main prey item, which are clams.

Two walrus (Odobenus rosmarus) hauled out on ice floe

4

British seals

Two species of seal are resident and breed in Britain – common seals, also known as harbour seals (*Phoca vitulina*) and grey seals (*Halichoerus grypus*).

Common seals occur in the north Atlantic and north Pacific and are divided into five different subspecies. The European subspecies, *Phoca vitulina vitulina* is found in the north-east Atlantic from Portugal to Iceland with the most northerly colony on Svalbard. There are about 83,000 common seals in Europe; 35% of these are found in the UK and 83% of these in Scotland.

Grey seals are found only in the north Atlantic, the Baltic Sea and the Barents Sea. They are one of the rarer seal species with a world population of only 350,000-400,000. About 40% of the world population live in the UK, and about 90% of these live in Scotland.

Scotland is clearly a good place for seals. This is due to a combination of:
- the wild and remote coastline, which provides safe places to haul ashore and to breed; and
- the rich foraging grounds of the Continental Shelf nearby.

Seal names

Common seals are often called '**harbour**' seals. Interestingly, common seals are less numerous than greys in Scotland, and greys are more often found in harbours! The scientific name for a common seal is *Phoca vitulina* meaning '**plump calf**' from the Greek 'phoce' meaning 'plump' (which is derived from the Sanskrit 'spha' meaning 'fat') and from the Latin 'vitulus' meaning 'calf'. In Shetland they used to be called '**tang fish**', being the seals usually found amongst the 'tang' or seaweed. In Gaelic they are called '**ron cumanta**'. Another old local name is '**black seal**', referring to their dark, newly moulted coat.

Grey seals should correctly be called **Atlantic grey seals**. Their scientific name is *Halichoerus grypus* which is derived from the Greek meaning '**sea-pig with a hooked nose**'. The old Shetland name is '**haaf fish**', as these were the seals seen at the offshore 'haaf' fishing grounds. They are called '**ron mor**' in Gaelic and '**horsehead**' in Canada.

Male seals are sometimes called '**bulls**', females are '**cows**' and young are '**calves**' or '**pups**'.

In Orkney and Shetland, seals are called '**selchies**' or '**selkies**' and this is the name most often encountered in mythical tales about seals.

Identifying common and grey seals

It can be very difficult to differentiate between common and grey seals, especially when they are in the water. Also, juvenile grey seals can look very like common seals. The main distinguishing features are the shape of the head and the pattern of the coat (though this can be very variable) and the size of adults. With practice and a good view of the animal, it is possible to tell the species apart, especially the adults, but some juvenile grey seals will always prove difficult.

Physical features

One of the easiest distinguishing features to see is the more rounded head of the common seal. Some guides say the shape of the nostrils is distinctive: common seals have V-shaped nostrils while in grey seals the nostrils are more parallel. This can be confusing as both can appear V-shaped, especially when the nostrils are flared when the seal is breathing. You also need to be quite close to see a seal's nostrils clearly!

Common seals have large eyes positioned more on the front of their face, closer to their nose than the back of the head. The forehead rises more steeply than the nose, giving them a dog-like or 'spaniel' appearance. The mouth is almost directly under their nose and they have slightly fleshy jowls, where their whiskers grow, which stick out slightly sideways.

Grey seals have a more oval head and a heavy muzzle, resembling that of a horse. They do not have the dip between their forehead and muzzle as do common seals. The muzzle becomes more pronounced with age, especially in males. Their eyes appear to be slightly on the side of their head, midway between the nose and the back of the head. Their mouth is tucked underneath and back from the tip of their fleshy snout. They often appear to have multiple chins.

Behaviour

On shore, common seals are virtually silent, other than during the breeding season when pups will call to their

An adult male grey seal showing its dark coat, heavy nose and multiple chins

mothers. Grey seals will frequently 'sing' when hauled ashore. They produce this eerie wail when they jostle for space on a haulout site. This unusual call may be one of the reasons behind some of the myths and stories associated with seals and with this species in particular.

Both species of seal often adopt a 'banana' shape, with their head and hind flippers held higher than the middle part of their body. They usually lie like this when the tide is rising. It seems they are keeping their hind flippers out of the water for as long as possible to reduce heat loss – there is very little insulating blubber in their flippers.

Common seals will occasionally porpoise through the water. Grey seals do not swim like this, though young greys will frolic in the water.

An adult common seal showing its spotted coat, dog-like face and prominent whiskers

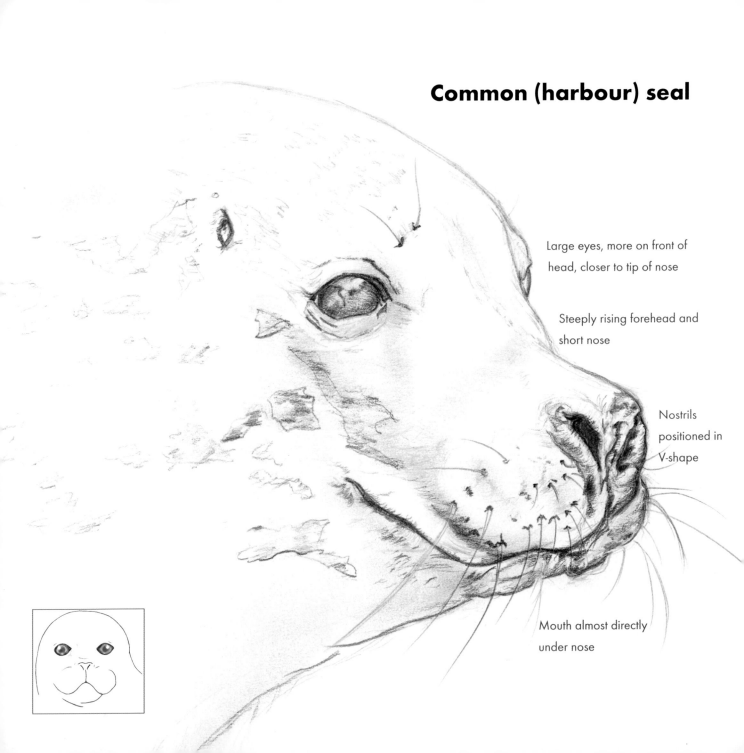

Common (harbour) seal

Large eyes, more on front of head, closer to tip of nose

Steeply rising forehead and short nose

Nostrils positioned in V-shape

Mouth almost directly under nose

Grey seal

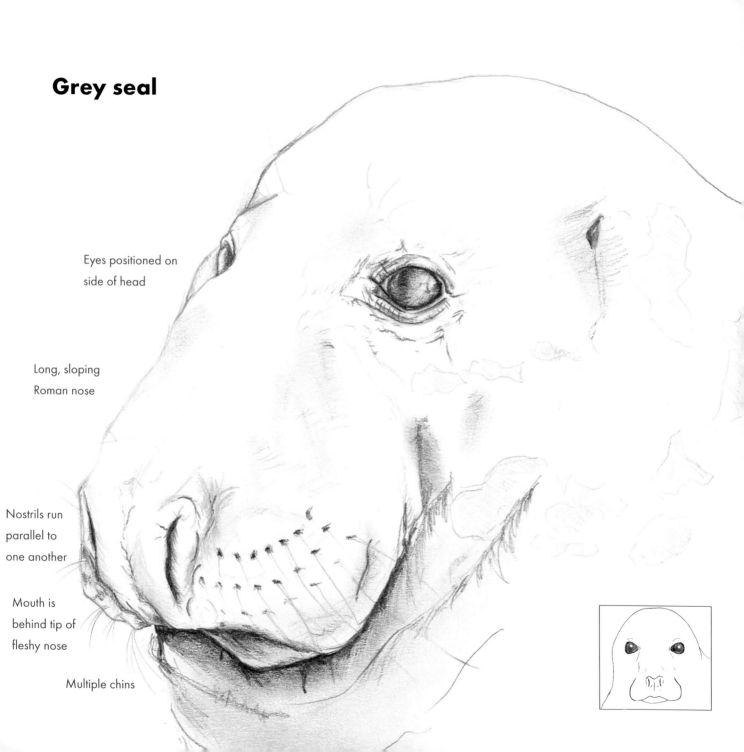

Eyes positioned on side of head

Long, sloping Roman nose

Nostrils run parallel to one another

Mouth is behind tip of fleshy nose

Multiple chins

Size

Adult common seal males weigh about 85kg and measure about 145cm in length. Females weigh about 75kg and are about 135cm long, not much smaller than males. In fact it is very difficult to tell males from females. You can sometimes see the penile aperture of males when they lie on their side or the two nipples of females. But remember that both sexes have quite a prominent umbilicus (navel)!

Grey seals are bigger than common seals; adult males can weigh up to 300kg and be 200cm long while adult females weigh up to 180kg and are about 180cm long. Males and females are quite different in other ways. Adult males have a heavier nose and their coats tend to be more uniformly dark in colour. Females are slighter and more two-toned in colour; their backs are darker grey than their bellies. The blotchy coat pattern is more conspicuous in females than in males.

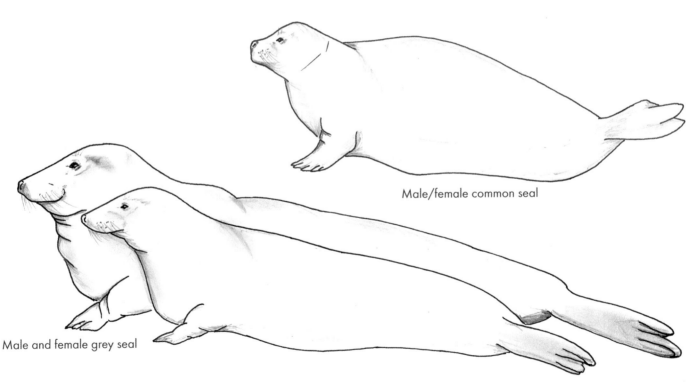

Male/female common seal

Male and female grey seal

Re-drawn from Peter Folkens poster on seals

Coat

The common seal's coat is mottled with lots of small spots. Although the pattern is very variable between individuals, it is fairly uniform over the whole body. The coat colour changes through the year, from fairly dark charcoal-grey when they have recently moulted, to pale sandy-brown shortly before they moult. Newborn pups are born in their first adult coat, which is quite dark.

Common seal with wet and dry areas on its coat

Common seal coat variations

Pup

Coat before moult

Coat following moult

Coat during moult

Grey seal coat variations

Pup

Blotchy coat

Counter shading for camoflauge in water

Dark coat of older bull

A grey seal's coat is blotchy rather than spotted and there is much variation between individuals. Pups are born with a fluffy, white coat, which they moult after about three weeks. The adult coat is counter-shaded with the upper part a darker grey than the lower. This shading makes a seal in the water less visible from above (when it blends in with the darker water below) and from below (when the paler belly is visible). Males develop a more uniformly darker coat as they get older.

A seal's coat looks very sleek and shiny with well-defined spots or blotches when wet, and more silky and fuzzy when dry.

Annual cycle

The annual cycle of common and grey seals follows a similar pattern though there are differences in timing between the two species. Females give birth on land to a single pup (twins are very rare). Two to three weeks later they come into oestrus and mate with at least one male. Mothers produce very fat-rich milk and pups wean at three to five weeks of age before departing independently to sea. There does not appear to be any parental care after the pups are weaned. Adults begin their annual moult shortly after they have finished breeding.

Common and grey seals alternate trips to the sea when they search for food, with spells ashore when they rest at particular favoured locations on land. These resting areas are known as haulout sites.

Common seals

Common seals spend less time on shore and more time out at sea during the winter than during the summer. As summer approaches, they spend longer on shore at haulout sites, especially at low tide when isolated rocks or sandbanks are exposed. In June and

Common seal pup born in first adult coat

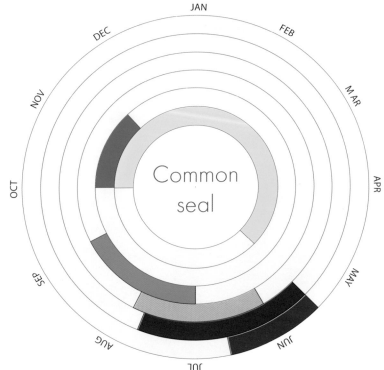

12

Grey seal pup born with white coat

early July, pregnant females tend to disperse from the main haulout groups and give birth to their pup, either alone or in very small groups. They spend longest ashore when moulting their coat, between July and September. In general, juveniles begin their moult first, followed by adults females, and then adult males, although there is considerable overlap between these groups.

Grey seals

Grey seals breed during the autumn months between September and early December. The timing of their moult is also dependent on age and sex and extends from December through to April. Their distribution during the breeding season, when they aggregate at traditional colonies, is quite different from that at other times of the year.

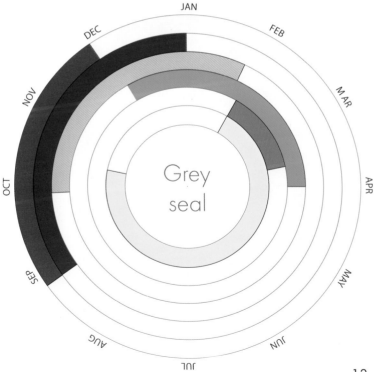

Pups are born   Moulting

Pup feeding   Embryo implants

Mating   Actual gestation

13

Breeding

Common seals

Common seal pups are usually born below the high tide mark and with their first adult coat, having moulted their white natal coat, or lanugo, in the uterus before being born. Common seal pups are, necessarily, quite advanced at birth and are able to swim with their mothers at the next incoming tide. Many females return each year to the same breeding site to give birth before mating about three weeks later. Mating is very seldom observed as it usually takes place in the water. Males defend underwater territories and attract females into their territories by calling under water. They produce a bizarre sound. Imagine combining the sound of an approaching freight train with that of a ball rolling down a bowling alley and smashing into the skittles. Males display at one particular spot and may call once or twice before returning to the surface to breathe. Their display sometimes includes slapping the surface of the water with their fore flipper and thrashing pieces of seaweed around. Between June and August, males often have wounds on their heads, necks and hind flippers, resulting from underwater fights with other males. People used to think that common seals mated

Battle-scarred common seal

after their moult in September when seals were also seen thrashing seaweed. This is more likely to be young males practising for future years.

Grey seals

Grey seals breed in the autumn and, unlike common seals, they congregate at traditional breeding colonies, returning to the same place in the same colony in successive years. Many females even return to the same colony at which they were born. The precise timing of pupping depends on the location of the breeding colony. Breeding is earliest at colonies in the south-west of Britain and gets progressively later in a clockwise direction around the coast. Thus grey seals breed earliest in colonies in the Inner Hebrides, later in colonies in the Outer Hebrides, later still in Orkney and latest in colonies in east Sutherland and in the Firth of Forth. Grey seal pups have a white coat at birth because they used to breed on ice and this acted as camouflage. They still breed on ice in the Gulf of St Lawrence, Canada and in the Baltic Sea.

Male grey seals defend groups of females on land. They partly defend a piece of ground in a breeding colony and partly the females that use that piece of ground. They try to prevent females from leaving the area but, depending on the topography of the location and the determination of the female, this can be difficult. Territorial males are more successful at repelling other males from intruding into their territory to access any females that might be ready to mate. Fights between males can be violent and may result in serious injury. Fights occur on land or in the water as many territories include part of the coast. Mating can take place on land, in the shallows or in deeper water. The male usually bites the nape of the female's neck while mating and grips her with his fore flippers to prevent her from moving too much or escaping.

Male grey seal biting and clasping the female whilst mating in shallow water

Common seal under water showing its streamlined body, large eyes and prominent whiskers

Adaptations to life in the water

Seals have a number of special adaptations that allow them to remain under water without access to air (or oxygen) for sufficient time to find enough fish to eat.

Seals have very large lungs enabling them to exhale large amounts of carbon dioxide and inhale oxygen quickly and efficiently when they surface between dives. They have a very large blood volume relative to their body size. More blood means more haemoglobin, ensuring more oxygen can be carried in their blood stream. They also have a different oxygen-carrying pigment, myoglobin, in their muscles that can carry 40% more oxygen than haemoglobin, thus allowing even more oxygen to be stored in muscle tissue. Because they can carry so much oxygen in their blood and muscles, seals can restrict the blood flow to only their vital organs when diving, and also reduce their heart rate to only a few beats per minute. All these adaptations allow seals to maximise the amount of oxygen stored in their bodies and to minimise the rate at which it is used. Seals use up more energy when resting out of the water than when searching for food in water.

Seals are not affected by the increase in pressure as they dive under water. This is because they exhale before they dive and can collapse their lungs. They retain only a small volume of air (in gaseous form) that remains in their stiff-walled windpipe. This air is used to clear any water from around their nose when they next surface to breathe.

Seals have very large eyes to cope with reduced light levels, which helps them locate their food. They also use their sensitive whiskers to detect the slight changes in water movements made by swimming fish.

Seals have remarkably efficient kidneys that allow them to drink sea water. Only a few species of seal drink fresh water as well as sea water.

Seals are very well adapted to conserve body heat when swimming in cold water. These adaptations mean that they can overheat on hot days and need to move into the water to cool off.

SEALS

1. Highly streamlined body with thick blubber layer for insulation

2. Limbs specially adapted for swimming; one set for power, the other for steering

3. Large eyes that can see in low light conditions in and out of the water

4. Prominent whiskers for detecting prey under water, necessary in murky water

5. Large blood volume and very efficient oxygen storage mechanism in blood and muscle, enables seals to dive for prolonged periods without having to breathe

6. Blood is only pumped to vital organs when diving to conserve oxygen

7. Not affected by pressure under water as they exhale before diving and can collapse their lungs

8. Heart rate reduced from 80-120 beats per minute at surface down to 4-10 beats per minute when under water

9. Seals can drink sea water

DIVERS

1. Need wet or dry suit to protect against cold water. Body shape not streamlined

2. Require flippers for more efficient swimming. Steering not very easy

3. Need to trap a layer of air in a face-mask in order to see properly under water

4. Not applicable

5. Very limited capacity for breath holding. Need external supply of oxygen/air to remain under water for more than 1-4 minutes

6. Not applicable

7. Pressure severely limits dive depth and duration

8. Most people's heart rate will drop a small amount, even when putting their face in a basin of water

9. Water conservation a problem when in the sea for a long time

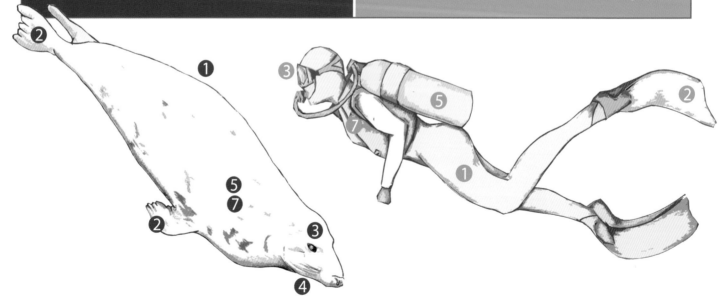

How deep can seals dive?

Although seals can dive to great depths and can remain underwater for an incredibly long time, most dive well within their capabilities, as deep and for as long as they need to find food. The record holder is the southern elephant seal, the biggest species, which has been recorded diving to over 2,000m and remaining under water for up to 2 hours! Elephant seals spend over 90% of their lives under water, only returning to the surface to breathe, and to the shore to moult and breed. On avarage they dive to about 450m for 25 minutes.

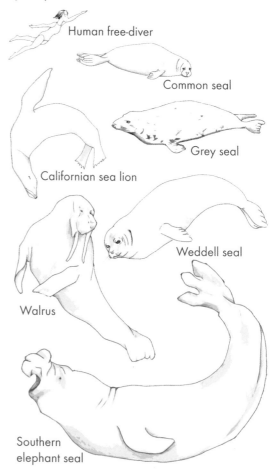

Human free-diver

Common seal

Grey seal

Californian sea lion

Weddell seal

Walrus

Southern elephant seal

Metres below sea level

| 0 |
| 100 |
| 200 |
| 300 |
| 400 |
| 500 |
| 600 |
| 700 |
| 800 |
| 900 |
| 1000 |
| 1100 |
| 1200 |
| 1300 |
| 1400 |
| 1500 |
| 1600 |
| 1700 |
| 1800 |
| 1900 |
| 2000 |

Average (top of arrow) and maximum (bottom of arrow) dive depths for different species

Female grey seal searching for food in serrated wrack

Feeding

Seals eat fish and are often regarded as undesirable competitors by all kinds of fishermen. In the open sea, seals are only one group of animals that eat fish. The main consumers of fish around Britain are: humans, cetaceans (whales, dolphins and porpoises), birds, fish and seals. In fact, there are more fish-eating harbour porpoises in the North Sea than there are seals of both species in the whole of the United Kingdom!

Dive records from common and grey seals show that both species of seal forage for fish on or close to the sea bed. They are able to dive down to 250m, but because they forage on the Continental Shelf, most dives are usually not as deep as this. Favourite prey species for common seals include sandeels, flatfish, white fish, cephalopods (mainly octopus) and members of the herring family (e.g. herring and sprats). Grey seals also eat a lot of sandeels, whitefish and flatfish. Grey and common seals do not appear to be active 'hunt and chase' predators. Rather, they seem to eat fish that are either abundant or that they happen to encounter. Diet composition varies around Britain and also varies seasonally, reflecting differences in the availability or abundance of the different fish species.

Shoal of sandeels, a favourite prey of seals

Where to find seals

Common seals

Common seals appear to favour slightly more sheltered parts of the Scottish coast. Their strongholds in Scotland are in Shetland, Orkney, the east coast of the Outer Hebrides, most of the Inner Hebrides and the west coast of Scotland (from Skye and Lochcarron down to Arran in the Firth of Clyde), the Moray Firth and the Firth of Tay. There are smaller numbers along the north coast, the far north-west coast and in the Firth of Forth.

Their distribution is similar during the breeding season and the main survey time (moult). During the breeding season, groups tend to be smaller and more dispersed. This is at least in part because females appear to prefer to give birth in isolation or in small groups away from the main haulout areas. There is almost no information on the winter distribution of common seals around Scotland, though at the locations which have been studied, their distribution is similar to the summer, with much smaller numbers ashore at any one time.

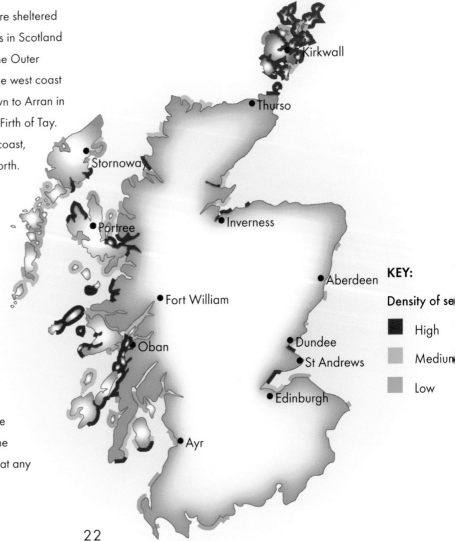

Lerwick

Kirkwall

Thurso

Stornoway

Inverness

Portree

Aberdeen

Fort William

Dundee

St Andrews

Oban

Edinburgh

Ayr

KEY:

Density of se

■ High

Mediun

Low

22

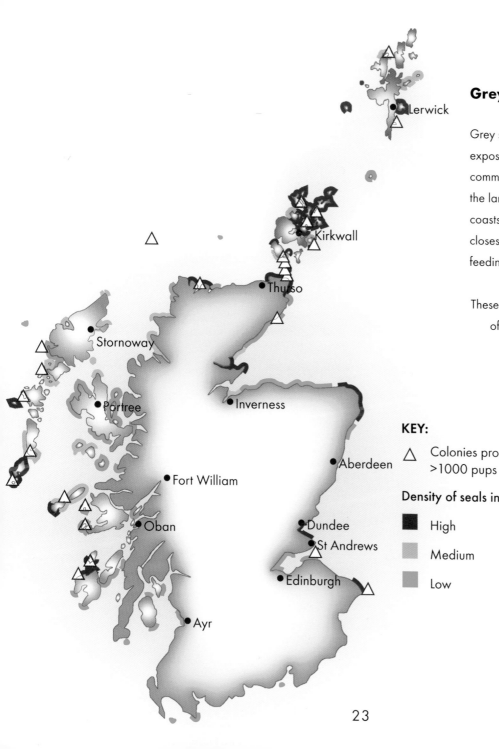

Grey seals

Grey seals seem to favour more exposed coasts and islands than common seals. In the summer months, the largest numbers are on the islands or coasts closest to the open sea, perhaps closest to their preferred offshore feeding areas.

These areas include the outer fringes of Shetland and Orkney, the west coast of the Outer Hebrides, outer islands in the Inner Hebrides, outer sandbanks in the Firth of Tay and the Moray Firth. During their autumn breeding season, grey seals congregate at traditional breeding colonies in the Inner and Outer Hebrides, Shetland, Orkney, a few places on the north and far north-east coast of mainland Scotland and in the Firth of Forth.

KEY:

△ Colonies producing >1000 pups

Density of seals in August

■ High

■ Medium

■ Low

Lerwick

Kirkwall

Thurso

Stornoway

Portree

Inverness

Aberdeen

Fort William

Oban

Dundee

St Andrews

Edinburgh

Ayr

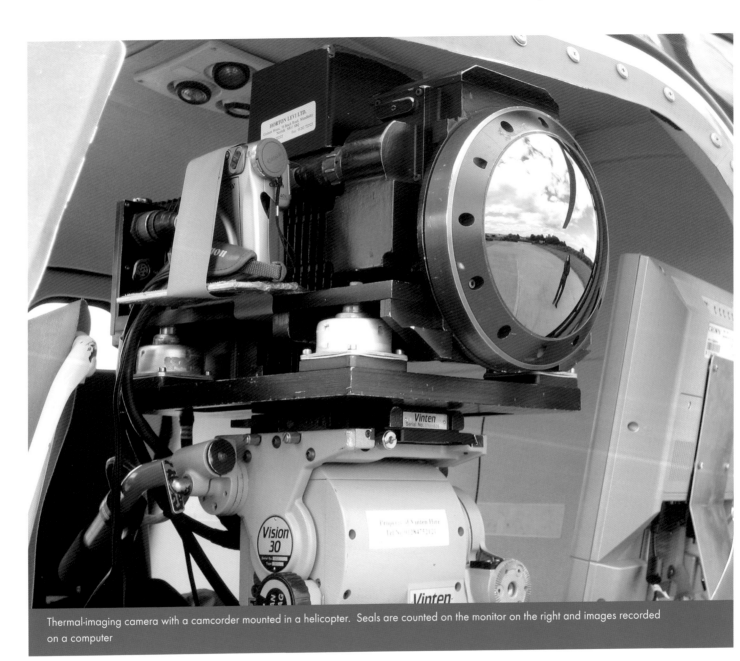

Thermal-imaging camera with a camcorder mounted in a helicopter. Seals are counted on the monitor on the right and images recorded on a computer

How many seals are there?

Monitoring seal distribution and population size

Common and grey seals are widely distributed around the coast of Scotland and there is considerable regional and seasonal variation in their abundance. Different aerial survey methods are used to monitor the numbers of common and grey seals hauled out. Common seals are counted during their annual moult, in August, when the largest numbers of seals are found on shore. Grey seals are counted at the same time, but these numbers are highly variable, and cannot be used to accurately estimate the size of their population. Instead, grey seals are surveyed during their autumn breeding season, when the numbers of pups born each year are counted.

Surveys are carried out from aircraft, both helicopter and fixed-wing. Common seals are very well camouflaged on shore but can be detected using a thermal-imaging camera normally mounted in a helicopter. Grey seals breed on remote islands and coasts, and breeding colonies are surveyed using large-format, vertical aerial photography between mid September and the end of November.

Thermal image (above) and aerial photograph (below) of the same site in Ungam, Shetland

Common seals

Common seals are counted around Scotland roughly on a five-year cycle, although seals in the Firth of Tay and the Moray Firth are counted more often. The number of seals counted represents the minimum size of the population, as an unknown number of seals will be at sea during the survey and therefore not counted.

Recent surveys show there are at least 23,500 common seals in Scotland, just under 90% of the total number found in Great Britain and Northern Ireland.

Counts are made during the period when the seals are moulting since they prefer to spend as long as possible out of the water at this time. About two thirds of the total population can be hauled out at any time during their annual moult.

Common seal fitted with satellite transmitter

Grey seals

The numbers of grey seal pups born at all the main breeding colonies in Scotland are surveyed every year using vertical aerial photography. After decades of year on year increase, pup production has stabilised at colonies on the west coast. It is still increasing in Orkney and North Sea colonies but at a slower rate.

Over 40,000 pups are born in Scotland each year. Translating the numbers of pups born into an estimate of the total population size is not straight forward. For the latest estimates of both pup production and total population size, refer to the Sea Mammal Research Unit's web site at: www.smru.st-and.ac.uk/scos

Satellite transmitter using mobile phone technology

Tracking techniques

When seals are on land they are relatively easy to observe and study. But, seals spend most of their lives out at sea, searching for fish. To find out where they go to feed, seals are tracked remotely using small computers which are glued to the back of their heads. These computers record various bits of information such as the dive profile, water temperature, swimming speed and location. All the information is stored until it can be transmitted, either via a satellite network or through a mobile phone network. This will be when the seal returns to the surface to breathe, hauls out, and/or comes within the range of the mobile phone network.

Common seals generally remain closer to the coast than grey seals. Each common seal seems to have its own particularly favoured foraging area to which it returns repeatedly on successive trips. Grey seals seem to behave similarly, though they often forage further off shore over the Continental Shelf. Seals can easily travel about 100 kilometres per day.

Each colour represents the movements of an individual common seal around the Shetland Islands; blue for males, red for females

Visiting seals and other species

A number of different seal species have been occasionally or rarely seen in Scotland. These are mostly Arctic species and include: walrus, harp, hooded, ringed and bearded seals. A walrus was reported in the Firth of Clyde, off Arran in August 2000, in early 2006 a ringed seal was seen in the Kyle of Sutherland and a young hooded seal in the mouth of the River Conon! The Shetland Marine Mammal Group regularly report sightings of bearded seals. It can be very difficult to identify these visiting species, especially if they remain in the water, so the actual frequency of occurrence may be slightly greater than is realised at present. If they haul ashore, differences in size, body shape and coat pattern can be used to identify different species.

Walrus - found in the Arctic waters around Greenland and Svalbard. They are large and pink, and have prominent tusks.

Harp seal - found mainly around Newfoundland, the north of Iceland, Greenland and up into the White Sea, off the Russian coast. Adults have a dark face mask and a harp shaped patch on their back. Pups are harvested in Canada.

Hooded seal - usually found in the north Atlantic but can be sighted as far south as the Caribbean. They are mostly dark with white blotches. It is an animal of deep water and heavy ice floes.

Ringed seal - the most common Arctic seal. It is found in fast-ice and is the only seal to construct a shelter in which to bear its young. The ringed seal is the main prey of polar bears. They have grey spots that are surrounded by a pale halo.

Bearded seal - has a similar distribution to the ringed seal, being found around all the European, Asiatic and American Arctic coasts, mainly in shallow waters. As its name suggests, it has particularly long, bushy whiskers. They are big seals with a large head on a small body.

Harp seal (*Phoca groenlandica*)

Hooded seal (*Cystophora cristata*) male displaying

Ringed seal (*Phoca hispida*)

Bearded seal (*Erignathus barbatus*)

Interactions between seals, fisheries and fish farms

Seals eat fish. Most of the time this is not an issue, but seals can and do cause problems to certain fisheries. Seals may enter rivers to eat salmon and sea trout, travelling as much as 20km upstream. Seals in Orkney raid the bait from pots set for crabs and lobsters. Fish caught or trapped in nets provide seals with a ready-caught, highly accessible meal. Sometimes seals only eat part of the fish or just bite out the oil-rich liver. This can cause understandable frustration to fishermen who are unable to sell the damaged fish.

Seals can also cause problems with the finfish farming industry. It is not surprising that seals are attracted by the large numbers of fish held in the stock cages. They may eat fish through the netting and sometimes get into the cages. Worst of all they can tear the netting, allowing the farmed fish to escape into the open sea. Not only does the fishfarmer lose his valuable stock, but there are serious concerns about the effects of farmed fish hybridising with native species. Modern net design, using stronger materials and stronger tensioning, has helped to reduce this problem.

Fish farm

30

Grey seal eating a salmon in a river

The Moray Firth Seal Management Plan

There is one Special Area of Conservation (SAC) for common seals and six for Atlantic salmon in the Moray Firth area. The Plan aims to rationalise the conservation of common seals in the Firth with the conservation of salmon, together with the commercial interests of the salmon sport angling industry and the few remaining salmon netsmen. A licence is issued by the Scottish Executive allowing shooting of a specified maximum number of common seals. This number is calculated to ensure that shooting will not adversely affect the overall viability of the common seal population in the Firth. Very strict conditions are attached to the licence; only seals within rivers (those that are likely to be eating salmon) can be shot, and there is a strict upper limit for the number of seals that may be shot in each river. The Plan includes an extensive research programme, part of which is investigating whether sonic scaring devices might be used to prevent seals from entering salmon rivers in the first place, thus negating the need for any shooting.

Threats to seals

Human related threats

The main anthropogenic threats to seals are from:

- excessive pollution (e.g. physical contamination from oil spills; pups are particularly vulnerable);
- toxic chemicals (e.g. organochlorines or brominated flame retardants that can be ingested and that accumulate in blubber);
- fishing/fish farms (e.g. shooting in salmon rivers or at fish farms);
- entanglement in offshore nets.

Female grey seal caught in a fine fishing net

In many rural communities, seals are regarded as undesirable, competitive pests. The salmon netting industry in Scotland has almost disappeared. This is partly due to a reduction in the number of salmon returning to rivers to spawn, and partly (some would argue), to the predation by seals of salmon caught in the nets.

Turbines

There is an ever increasing demand to produce energy from renewable sources. Scotland's highly dynamic coastline, continuously pounded by waves and surrounded by strong tidal streams, has enticed developers to investigate different methods of generating electricity from the sea. To extract energy from tidal streams, underwater turbines must be placed in areas with strong tidal flows, which are also often favoured feeding grounds for seals and other marine animals. The nature and scale of any response of seals to marine turbines, or the impact of turbines on seals, are unknown at present, and are being studied at various locations including Orkney and Northern Ireland.

Natural threats

Disease

In both 1988 and in 2002, common seals were affected by the phocine distemper virus (PDV). Approximately half the seals on the east coast of England, mainly around The Wash, died in 1988. Mortality was considerably lower in Scotland. In 2002, about 20% of seals in eastern England died, and even fewer were affected in Scotland. On both occasions, seals affected by the virus were first seen at the same location in Denmark. The English seal populations took some time to recover from the virus, but populations on continental Europe (i.e. the Netherlands, Germany, Denmark and Sweden) recovered very rapidly in the year following the outbreak. The virus had a serious impact on common seals but seemed to have little effect on grey seals.

Killer whales

In recent years, orca or killer whales have been seen more regularly in Shetland and Orkney, and have been observed feeding on both common and grey seals. The orca usually arrive towards the end of the common seal breeding season, in late June or early July, possibly to prey on the recently born pups. Interestingly, they are not seen as frequently during the grey seal breeding season when many more pups are available.

Climate change

The climate is changing and seals are likely to be affected. Common and grey seal populations range from northern France into the Arctic. They are clearly capable of living and breeding under a variety of climatic conditions. During development, a common or grey seal pup's first coat is white, an adaptation to avoid predation when they were born on ice. Common seals no longer breed on ice in the north Atlantic and pups now moult their white coat before they are born. Grey seals still breed on ice in part of their range, and elsewhere pups still retain their white coat for the first few weeks of life.

The most noticeable effect of climate change on seals is likely to be through changes in the distribution and the availability of their prey. The life-cycles of many fish are strongly linked to water temperature. If sea temperatures change, fish will either have to adapt to the change or alter their distribution. However, if one species moves out of a particular area another is likely to move in and occupy the vacated niche. Although they will eat whatever species of prey is available, the main food of common and grey seals is sandeels. If sandeel populations are adversely affected by climate change then seal populations might be also. Evidence suggests that sandeel populations are already responding to climate change.

Conservation legislation

The Conservation of Seals Act 1970 protects common seals from 1st June to 31st August and grey seals from 1st September to 31st December, during their respective breeding seasons. Recent Conservation Orders protect common seals throughout the year over most of the east coast and the Northern Isles; the one in the Moray Firth also includes grey seals. The Act defines the methods by which seals can be killed. Seals can only be killed during the protected period (known as the close season) under licence issued by the Scottish Executive. There is a move to update the Conservation of Seals Act in Scotland.

Under European legislation, both seal species are of 'Community Interest', meaning they are relatively uncommon across Europe as a whole. Under this legislation, known as the Habitats Directive, SNH have identified a number of Special Areas of Conservation (SACs) for common and grey seals. SACs were selected on the basis of the numbers of seals within each area combined with a reasonably even spread of areas around Scotland.

The Isle of May, off the Fife coast — an SAC for grey seals

History

Archaeological evidence

There is archaeological evidence of seals in some of the earliest human settlements around Scotland. The remains of common and grey seals have been found on Oronsay, off the west coast of Argyll, dating back to the Mesolithic period (6,000 – 5,000 years ago). Most of the remains from these sites were of grey seal pups. The sites appeared to be inhabited seasonally, mainly during early and mid summer, rather than throughout the year. It is possible that the inhabitants avoided the area during the grey seal breeding season so as not to disturb the seals and encourage them to continue breeding, thus providing a reliable harvest before the onset of winter.

This evidence from the past suggests that grey seals must have bred somewhere on Oronsay or very nearby. There are currently two important breeding colonies on Eilean nan Ron (the island of the grey seal) and Eilean Ghaoideamal, both of which are very close to the excavation site.

The remains of only one common seal were found at the Oronsay excavation. Presumably common seals were less numerous or perhaps harder to hunt. Breeding grey seals will move inland some distance from the water's edge making them more accessible to hunters.

Seal bones have been found in Orkney, Shetland and near Applecross, Wester Ross. There are accounts of people rowing from Orkney out to Sule Skerry, 60km to the west, to harvest seals, implying that there were very few in Orkney at that time.

Exploitation

Seals would have provided an important resource for indigenous peoples in the past. They are large animals whose carcasses would have provided strong, waterproof skin for boats and shelters; oil for carbohydrates, burning and lighting; and meat for eating. Their bones were less useful as they were not as dense or hard wearing as bones from land animals such as deer or wild boar. Until the middle of the 19th century seal oil was used on Colonsay to light the lamps in the Old Manse, and seal skin was also used to make boots until Wellington boots became more popular! Common seals were harvested until the early 1980s for their skins, which were used in the manufacture of sporrans.

Watching seals

Inquisitive grey seals

Seals are naturally inquisitive and if you remain relatively calm and still they will often come to you; you don't have to go right up to them. They are more wary and easily disturbed when they are hauled out on shore and much more inquisitive when they are in the sea. Grey seals in particular may swim to within a few metres of you.

Take care when approaching groups of seals on land. If you can see them looking at you and getting agitated, perhaps beginning to shuffle down to the edge of the water, you are getting too close and very soon they will stampede into the sea. If one seal goes, others will follow, whether they have seen you or not. Retreat a little until the seals settle down. Be aware of the wind direction; seals have a keen sense of smell and they will detect you earlier if you are upwind of them.

Please do not disturb!

Seals are particularly vulnerable to disturbance during the breeding season and, to a lesser extent, during their moult. Mothers recognise their pups from their calls and smell. The bond formation between mother and pup can be interrupted by excessive or persistent disturbance, particularly during the first few days after birth. If a mother fails to recognise her pup and abandons it, the pup is likely to starve and die. Females pupping for their first time are often more susceptible to disturbance.

During their moult, seals prefer to spend longer out of the water than at other times of the year. This is because they are growing new hair. At this time their peripheral blood supply is open, providing the cells that make the new hair with the necessary nutrients. If they are forced to enter the water the blood system closes down and they have to restart this system when they next haul out. This is a drain on their energy reserves.

Where to watch seals

There are some excellent boat operators who organise trips to see seals at close quarters. Check the local press, advertments around harbours and the local tourist office for details and contact numbers.
Some of the more accessible places are:
- Tentsmuir, just south of the Tay Estuary
- Orkney
- Shetland
- Western Isles, especially on the east coast of the Uists
- Moray Firth, on sandbanks exposed at low tide
- Mull, particularly around the more sheltered parts
- Skye and Lochcarron
- West coast of Strathclyde Region.

You can get close views of seals from a boat especially if you remain quiet and move slowly

What to do if you find a seal on shore

Seals have to haul on shore to rest after spending time at sea. Young seals that are still learning what the sea has to offer, or that are still being cared for by their mother, sometimes haul on shore at unusual sites, including beaches that are popular with humans.

If the seal is obviously uninjured, the best thing to do is to leave it alone and give it some space. Be particularly careful with dogs that are not on a lead. In time the seal should return to the sea on its own. Very young seals may be waiting for their mothers to return. It is very important not to disturb or to handle them. The mother may be scared by the smell of humans on her pup and may abandon it. Remember that seals can, and do, bite!

If you find an injured seal, call the SSPCA who will remove the seal for appropriate treatment.

If you find a dead seal on shore, your local council has the responsibility of disposing of the carcass. If the carcass is very fresh, you could inform the veterinarians at the Scottish Agricultural College, Inverness and the Sea Mammal Research Unit, University of St Andrews. Be sure to give precise details of the location of the carcass, preferably with a gird reference.

A grey seal pup waiting patiently for its mother to return

The Scottish Marine Wildlife Watching Code

This recently produced code provides information and advice on the best way to observe marine mammals. www.marinecode.org/documents/Scottish-Marine–Code-web.pdf

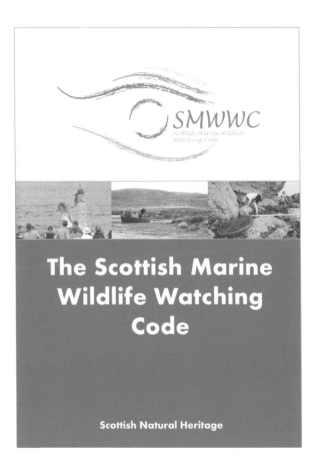

Key points:

- Be aware of how close you are to seals hauled out on shore. Do not approach too close. Use binoculars or a telescope to get a better view.

- Seals are more approachable when they are in the water.

- Be aware of the seals' reaction to you. Are they agitated or relaxed? Try to leave them relaxed.

- Do not surround a group of seals. Try to get everyone to approach from one direction and leave the seals an obvious escape route to the sea.

- Be particularly careful during the breeding season (June and July for common seals and September to December for grey seals).

- If you are in a boat or kayak, approach seals slowly and carefully, assessing their reaction to you. Be visible from a distance so that seals are not surprised by your presence, and move away slowly if they begin to get agitated.

Myths and legends

Myths and legends about seals or selkies (their Orcadian name) abound in the areas where seals are most abundant, especially in Shetland, Orkney and the Western Isles. The tales are often based on a common theme – the seal-folk could transform into humans by shedding their skins when they came onto the land. The skin had to be carefully hidden or kept close at hand, because without it the selkie could not return to its seal form and its life in the sea. The transformed seal-folk were always very beautiful and alluring, but would never stop searching for their hidden sealskin as they invariably preferred life in the sea to life on land.

Male seals came ashore in search of either single or married human females. Walter Traill Dennison, the 19th century Orkney folklorist wrote that they '*often made havoc among thoughtless girls, and sometimes intruded into the sanctity of married life*'. Girls who were last seen alone on the foreshore at low tide were thought to have been taken by the selkie folk. The ballad of the grey selkie from Sule Skerry is a sad story about a young woman who bears a son to a selkie man (see page 42).

Female seals were kidnapped by men in search of a beautiful wife. If a female shed her skin on land and it was captured by a snooping man, she was bound to him until she could find, or was given back, her skin. The children born from selkie marriages were usually the most beautiful in the district.

Oh, handsome man, if there is any mercy in your human breast, give me back my sealskin. I cannot live in the sea without it. I cannot live among my own people without my sealskin.

The Goodman o 'Wastness is a fine Orcadian story about such a marriage.

As soon as the seal was clear of the water, it reared up and its skin slipped down to the sand. What had been a seal was a white-skinned boy.

Pictures in the Cave, George Mackay Brown, 1979.

'The Selkie' - Leila Thomson's wonderful Orcadian tapestry. Hoxa Tapestry Gallery, Orkney

The Great Selkie o' Suleskerry

I heard a mother lull her bairn,
and aye she rocked, and aye she sang.
She took so hard upon the verse
that the heart within her body rang.

"O, cradle row, and cradle go,
and aye sleep well, my bairn within;
I ken not who thy father is,
nor yet the land that he dwells in."

And up then spake a grey selchie
as aye he woke her from her sleep,
"I'll tell where thy bairn's father is:
he's sittin' close by thy bed feet.

"I am a man upon the land;
I am a selchie on the sea,
and when I'm far frae ev'ry strand,
my dwelling is in Sule Skerry.

"And foster well my wee young son,
aye for a twal'month and a day,
and when that twal'month's fairly done,
I'll come and pay the nourice fee."

And when that weary twal'month gaed,
he's come tae pay the nourice fee;
he had ae coffer fu' o' gowd,
and anither fu' o' the white money.

"Upon the skerry is thy son;
upon the skerry lieth he.
Sin thou would see thine ain young son,
now is the time tae speak wi' he."

"But how shall I my young son know
when thou ha' ta'en him far frae me?"
"The one who wears the chain o' gowd,
'mang a' the selchies shall be he.

"And thou will get a hunter good,
and a richt fine hunter I'm sure he'll be;
and the first ae shot that e'er he shoots
will kill baith my young son and me."

This ballad was first written down in
1938 by Dr Otto Andersson, who heard
it sung on the island of Flotta.

Female grey seal on wave exposed boulder shore

Finding out more about seals

General books

Anderson, S. 1988. *Grey seal.* Shire Natural History Series, Thomas & Sons, Haverfordwest.

Anderson, S. 1990. *Seals.* Whittet Books, London.

Bonner, N. 1989. *The Natural History of Seals.* Christopher Helm (Publishers) Ltd., Kent.

King, J. 1983. *Seals of the World.* British Museum and Oxford University Press, London and Oxford.

Lister-Kaye, J. 1979 . *Seal Cull.* Penguin Books.

Thompson, D. 2002. *The People of the Sea.* Counterpoint.

Thompson, P. 1988. *Common seal.* Shire Natural History Series, Thomas & Sons, Haverfordwest.

Sources of further information

Scottish Agricultural College
SAC Veterinary Services, Drummondhill, Stratherrick Road, Inverness, IV2 4JZ. Tel: 01463 243 030
www.sac.ac.uk/consultancy/veterinary/contact/dsc/inverness

Scottish Society for the Prevention of Cruelty to Animals (SSPCA). Animal helpline: 0870 73 777 22
www.scottishspca.org

Sea Mammal Research Unit
University of St Andrews, St Andrews, Fife, KY16 8LB.
Tel: 01334 462 630
www.smru.st-and.ac.uk
(A series of information leaflets about seals can be found on the SMRU website)

Shetland Marine Mammal Group
www.nature-shetland.co.uk/seamammal

The Moray Firth Seal Management Plan
www.speyfisheryboard.com/spey_Moray_Firth_Seal_Plan

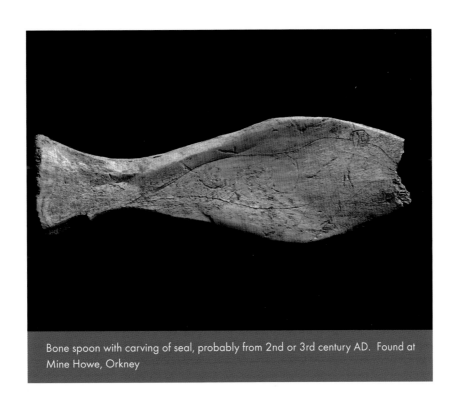

Bone spoon with carving of seal, probably from 2nd or 3rd century AD. Found at Mine Howe, Orkney

Also in the Naturally Scottish series...

Scotland has more than 65,000 native species of animals and plants. This series of colourful booklets looks at different aspects of this rich natural heritage from individual species, and even the genetic variations within them, to whole groups within different environments.

Amphibians & Reptiles

Although there are only six amphibians and three reptiles native to Scotland, these delightful animals have been part of our culture for a long time. They feature on Pictish stones and in a play - 'The Puddock and the Princess'.
John Buckley
ISBN 1 85397 401 3 pbk 40pp £4.95

Corncrakes

Secretive, skulking, rasping, loud, tuneless, scarce . . . all these words have been used to describe the corncrake. But once you could have added plentiful and widespread to the list. Now only a few birds visit Scotland each year. This booklet brings you the latest information on the corncrake and reveals this elusive and noisy bird in its grassy home.
Helen Riley and Rhys Greene
ISBN 1 85397 049 2 pbk 28pp £3.95

Bumblebees

Did you know that Bummiebee, Droner and Foggie-toddler are all Scottish names for the bumblebee? Find out what these names mean and why bumblebees are so special inside this beautifully illustrated booklet. Also discover how you can help the bumblebee by planting appropriate flowers for their continued survival.
Murdo Macdonald
ISBN 1 85397 364 5 pbk 36pp £4.95

Fungi

Fungi belong to one of the most varied, useful and ancient kingdoms in the natural world. Scotland may have almost 2000 larger species with some of the most interesting found in our woodlands and grasslands. This booklet provides an introduction to their life cycles, habitats and conservation. Discover the fascinating forms of earthstars, truffles and waxcaps.
Roy Watling MBE and Stephen Ward
ISBN 1 85397 341 6 pbk 36pp £4.95

Butterflies

There are 30 resident species of butterflies found in Scotland, as well as three regular migrants. The colourful adults may survive for just a few weeks but they certainly brighten up our lives.
Paul Kirkland
ISBN 1 85397 446 8 pbk 35pp £4.95

Lichens

There are more than 1700 species of lichen occuring throughout the British Isles, and many grow in Scotland where the air is purer. Several different species may be found on a single rock or tree, resulting in lichenologists spending hours in one spot!
Oliver Gilbert
ISBN 1 85397 373 4 pbk 40pp £4.95

Mosses & Liverworts

There are almost 1,000 species of moss and liver-wort growing in Scotland, representing more than 60% of the European bryophyte flora. Although they are small plants, they are certainly important ecologically and are also very beautiful.
Gordon Rothero
ISBN 1 85397 446 3 pbk 40pp £4.95

Sea Eagles

A well-organised reintroduction program has brought the sea eagle back to Scotland. This colourful booklet tells a wonderful story, which is illustrated by some of the finest natural history photographers in Europe.
ISBN 1 85397 461 7 pbk 34pp £4.95

Red Kites

This graceful and distinctive bird was absent from Scotland's skies for more than a century. Now with the help of a successful programme of re-introduction, its russet plumage and forked tail can once again be seen in Scotland.
David Minns and Doug Gilbert
ISBN 1 85397 210 X pbk 24pp £3.95

Dragonflies and damselflies

It follows the same format as other subjects in the Naturally Scottish series, describing what is special about the 23 species of Dragonflies and Damselflies that occur in Scotland and the particular habitats in which they are found. Their complex life cycle is explained and what they feed on. How you can help these beautiful insects and how to find out more about them is also included.
www.snh.org.uk/pubs   FREE

River Runners

Scotland's clean, cascading rivers contain a fas-cinating array of species. The atlantic salmon is the best known of our riverine species but others, such as lampreys and freshwater pearl mussels, are frequently overlooked but no less captivating. This booklet aims to illuminate aspects of their intriguing and largely unseen lifecycles, habitats and conservation measures.
Iain Sime
ISBN 1 85397 353 X pbk 44pp £4.95

Stoneworts

Stoneworts, or charophytes as they are sometime known, are a unique form of algae. They have a very complex structure which resembles many underwater higher plants much more than the filamentous blanketweeds and other simpler algae. They are often treated as honorary higher plants and as a result much more is known about their ecology and distribution than most other freshwater algae.
www.snh.org.uk/pubs   FREE

SNH Publications Order Form:
Naturally Scottish Series

Title	Price	Quantity
Amphibians & Reptiles	£4.95	....
Bumblebees	£4.95	....
Butterflies	£4.95	....
Corncrakes	£3.95	....
Fungi	£4.95	....
Lichens	£4.95	....
Mosses & Liverworts	£4.95	....
Red Kites	£3.95	....
River Runners	£4.95	....
Sea Eagles	£4.95	....
Seals	£4.95	....

Postage and packing: free of charge in the UK, a standard charge of £2.95 will be applied to all orders from the European Union. Elsewhere a standard charge of £5.50 will be applied for postage.

Please complete in BLOCK CAPITALS

Name _____

Address _____

_____

_____

Post Code _____

Type of Credit Card   VISA ☐   MasterCard ☐

Name of card holder

Card Number ☐☐☐☐ ☐☐☐☐ ☐☐☐☐ ☐☐☐☐

Expiry Date ☐☐☐☐

Send order and cheque made payable to Scottish Natural Heritage to:
Scottish Natural Heritage. Design and Publications, Battleby, Redgorton, Perth PH1 3EW

pubs@snh.gov.uk
www.snh.org.uk

Please add my name to the mailing list for the: SNH Magazine ☐
Publications Catalogue ☐